We created Color Noir because our culture, our stories, and our beauty are all tremendously important and deserve to be celebrated.

Each year we hear valid cries & complaints that the Oscars, the Grammys, and *insert organization X* are downplaying us, and not providing sufficient representation despite our undeniable excellence.

...and while that is absolutely true, instead of waiting for them, why don't we just do it ourselves???

We've put a ton of time, energy, our own resources into Color Noir, and we truly hope you enjoy it as much as we do. Can't wait to see what you create.

Much love!

Muoyo & Nicaila Okome

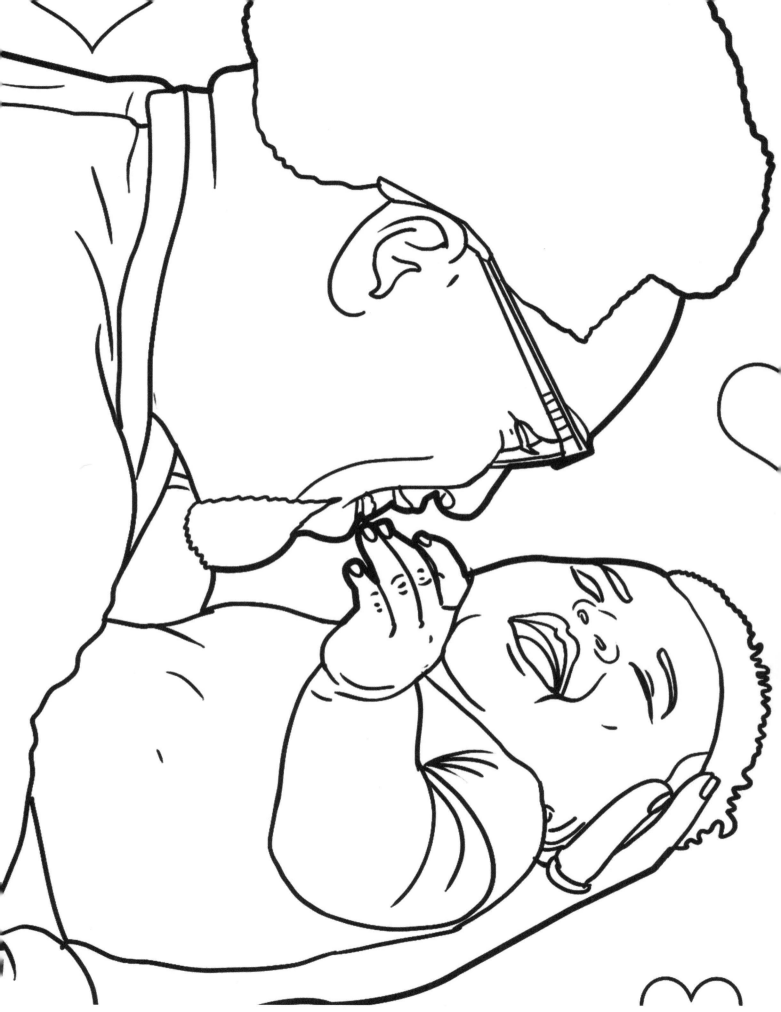

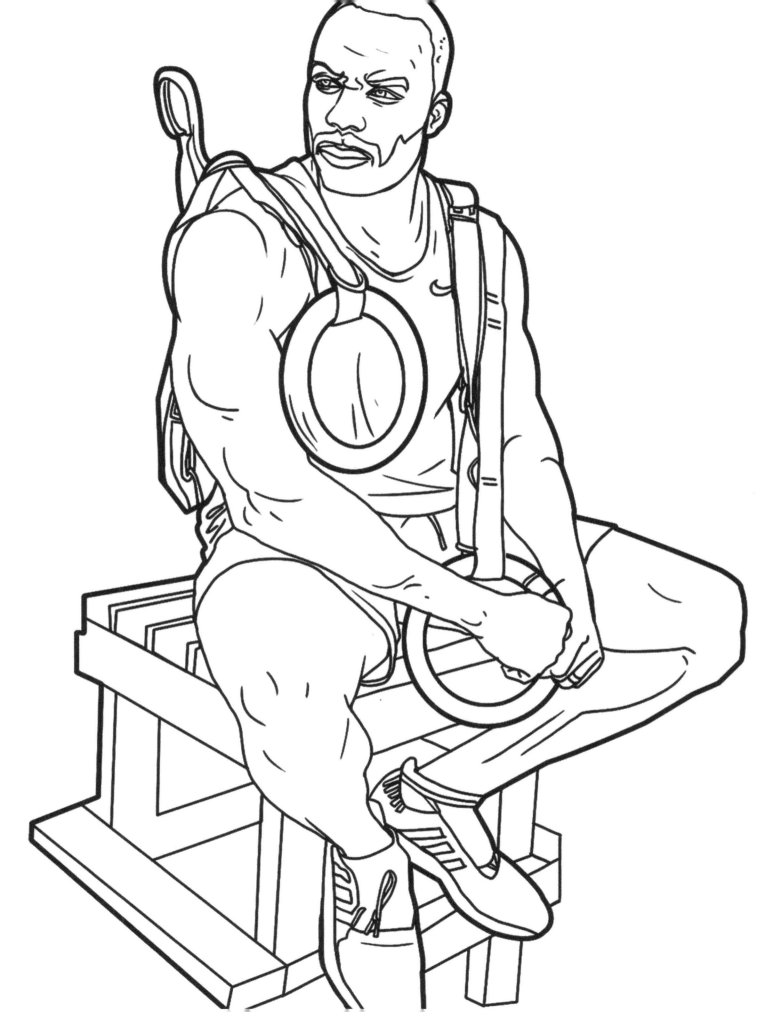

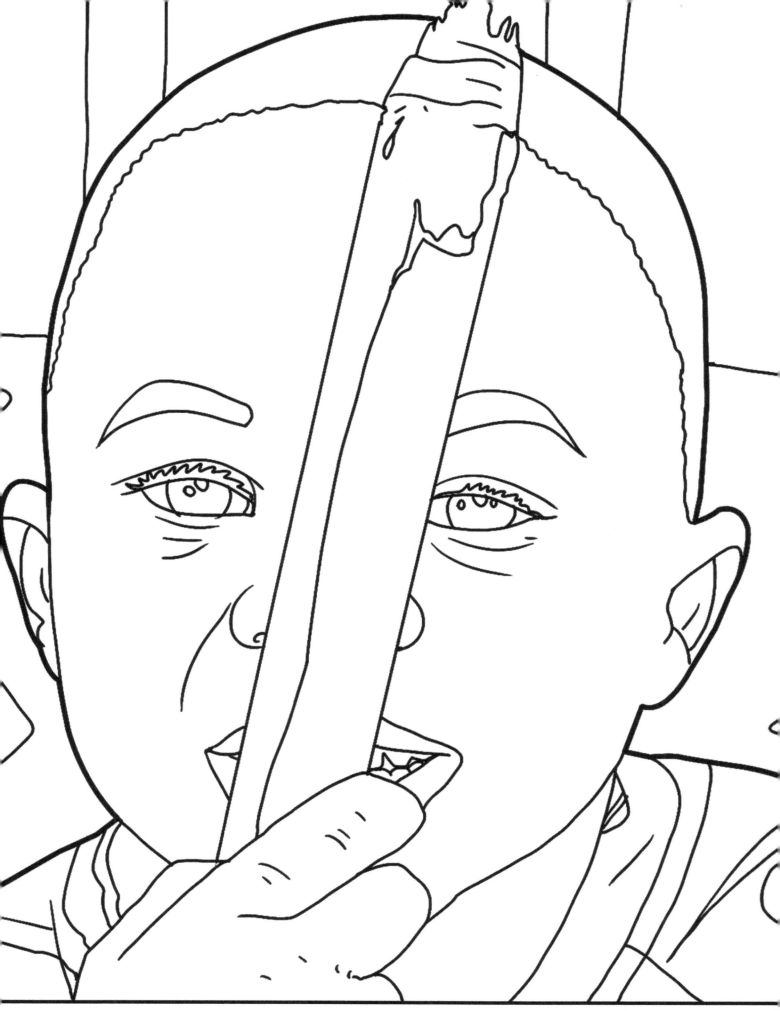

CPSIA information can be obtained
at www.ICGtesting.com
Printed in the USA
LVHW070817031121
702288LV00022B/289